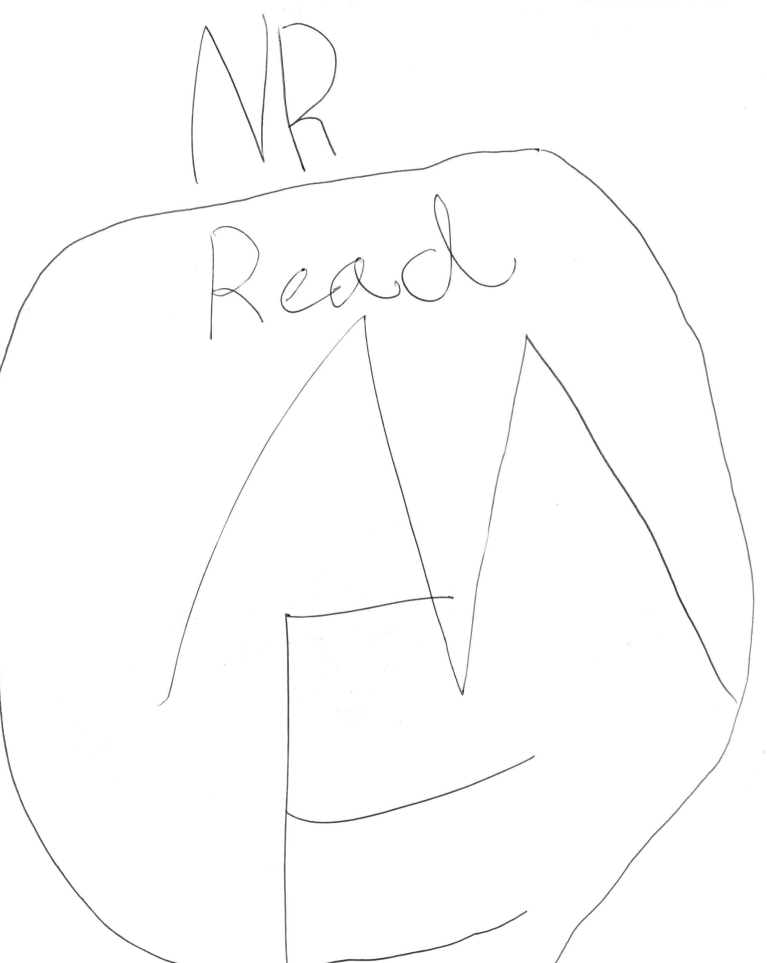

Library of Congress Control Number: 2005901962

ISBN 09618292-30

StarMist Books
starmistbooks@comcast.net

For my Mother

And for the little cat Jamile
and all like him

THE
GIFT
OF YOU

THE
GIFT
OF ME

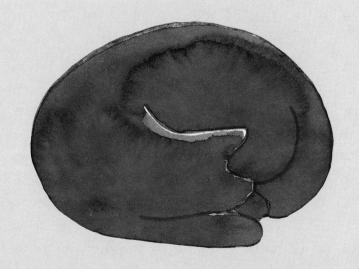

At the end of the lane

Stand two trees

Side by side

As their branches touch

And reach out wide

As each day ends

Jamile walks down the lane

Toward his tree friends

And he hears them murmuring

"Thank you rain

And thank you sun."

"Thank you," they whisper

In harmony

"For the ring

Around the moon at night

For the western sky

And the northern lights

Thank you for

The air we breathe

For the wild garden

And the flowered wreath

For the salty scent of the deep blue ocean

And for open spaces

Where flowers open

Thank you for

A place of peace

A place of dreams

And a place of sleep

Thank you for the ancient stones

For sand and sea

And a place called home

Thank you for

The color of joy

And the shape of love

For the shadows at dusk

For the mourning dove

Who coos in hours of gray

When life is sad

And we've lost our way

Thank you for life

And death

And life again

For the seed of hope

Born of each sad end

Thank you for the smallest gifts

For a sleeping cat

For a dog running free

For toes and clothes

And a sweet memory

And thank you for

Our friend

Jamile."

And Jamile smiled

When he heard his name

He hugged the trees

And walked down the lane.

One day it rained very hard.

Jamile tried to walk down the lane

To see his tree friends

But the wind and water

Floated him back

To his blue room.

He shivered and shook

And couldn't get warm

He felt lonely

And forlorn

For the voices

Of the trees

And sadness came

And sat with him

As he rested in bed

And heard the rain.

And the words of the trees

Then came to him

For once they had whispered

"We will be your friends

Even when you feel like

You have no friends

And if you can't find us

Because the road is dark

Remember to thank your

Self, that you have traveled this far

Along your path

And in your heart."

As he rested in bed

Tired and cold

He looked around his blue room

And within the blue

He saw many different blues

Dancing

Together

In harmony.

And he thought

Thank you, eyes,

That let us see

The blues

Of the nighttime sky

Thank you, ears,

That let us hear

The sound of the rain

Upon the lane

Thank you, hands,

For reaching out

Over sadness

And over doubt

Toward all

That is of wonder

Thank you, voice,

That lets me say

Love and peace

To you, today,

Who have walked down the lane

And sat with the trees

Who know the secret

That makes us free:

The gift of you

And the gift of me.

For believing, loving,

Feeling, seeing,

The gift of Earth

The miracle of being.

About the Author

Nila J. Webster resides on the North Shore of Massachusetts. Her textbook for high school students, *Literature for the Journey* (Council for Spiritual and Ethical Education), was published in 1992 and continues to be used in the classroom. An essay of hers appeared in *More Random Acts of Kindness* (Conari Press). Her stories and poetry have been published in local periodicals and literary anthologies. In 1996, she wrote the introduction to *silhouette of a soul*, a collection of poetry by jani johe webster, her mother. *The Gift of You, The Gift of Me* is the author's first picture book. She has also co-authored two picture books with her mother: *Remember Rain and Songs of Wonder for the Night Sea Journey* and *Remember Beauty and Songs for a Blue Time*.

About the Artist

George M. Ulrich has been illustrating children's books professionally since 1973. He has also authored several books for children which carry his own artwork, including *Mrs. Picasso's Polliwog* (Images Press) and *The Spook Matinee* (Delacourte Press). George and his wife Suzanne, an artist, live on the North Shore of Massachusetts. The artwork for *The Gift of You, The Gift of Me* was chosen by the Society of Illustrators for the Original Art 2006 Exhibition, and has been on display at the Museum of American Illustration.